S0-CBK-307

Scrambled Word Building™ Activity Book Grade 1

Table of Contents

Introduction 2
Possible Answers Found in the Activities 3

Activity Index

Activity 1	stamp	.4	Activity 32	number	.35
Activity 2	swing	.5	Activity 33	peanut	.36
Activity 3	wagon	.6	Activity 34	zipper	.37
Activity 4	apron	.7	Activity 35	donkey	.38
Activity 5	shovel	.8	Activity 36	crayon	.39
Activity 6	earth	.9	Activity 37	people	.40
Activity 7	grade	.10	Activity 38	jacket	.41
Activity 8	paste	.11	Activity 39	pillow	.42
Activity 9	peace	.12	Activity 40	puppet	.43
Activity 10	arrow	.13	Activity 41	yellow	.44
Activity 11	awake	.14	Activity 42	basket	.45
Activity 12	bacon	.15	Activity 43	family	.46
Activity 13	beach	.16	Activity 44	friend	.47
Activity 14	bread	.17	Activity 45	helped	.48
Activity 15	candy	.18	Activity 46	ladder	.49
Activity 16	chase	.19	Activity 47	Monday	.50
Activity 17	clean	.20	Activity 48	ribbon	.51
Activity 18	dance	.21	Activity 49	summer	.52
Activity 19	drink	.22	Activity 50	teach	.53
Activity 20	house	.23	Activity 51	across	.54
Activity 21	apple	.24	Activity 52	animal	.55
Activity 22	plant	.25	Activity 53	danger	.56
Activity 23	party	.26	Activity 54	return	.57
Activity 24	brown	.27	Activity 55	orange	.58
Activity 25	smile	.28	Activity 56	monkey	.59
Activity 26	phone	.29	Activity 57	square	.60
Activity 27	toast	.30	Activity 58	person	.61
Activity 28	world	.31	Activity 59	beaver	.62
Activity 29	hotel	.32	Activity 60	kitten	.63
Activity 30	finger	.33	Activity 61	pocket	.64
Activity 31	mitten	.34			

Introduction

The *Scrambled Word Building™ Activity Book* offers a fun and exciting way for children to learn to spell and read. These activities have been designed to be used as either homework assigned by a teacher, or with a parent. Before sending the activities home as homework, it would be helpful to go through an activity or two with the class as a whole, so children will know how to complete the activities.

Each activity in this book consists of four parts:

Look For:

At the top of the activity page, children are provided with a set of letters to work with. The same letters are printed in boxes across the side of the activity sheet. Children will cut these letters out and manipulate them to build words. These letters will be used to form as many words as possible. Eventually, all the letters will be used to make the "Scrambled Word." *Note: If you are using this activity book at home, we have included two complete alphabet letter sets. These letters can be used instead of cutting the letters on each activity page. We have also included an envelope at the end of the book to store the letters that have been used.*

Build It:

The *Build It* section prompts the child to write down the words they have built. The blank lines, ranging from 2-5 letter word possibilities, indicate the number of letters needed to spell each word. *Note: There may be more words that can be built than the number of blank spaces available.* As the child decodes and builds several words, they will figure out the "Scrambled Word" by using all the letters in the activity. Parents and teachers are encouraged to get involved and help with this section, as some first graders may find this to be a challenge.

Focus On:

This section provides extra word building practice by having the children focus on identifying the words they have built from the scrambled word and placing those new words in their appropriate category. The categories focus on initial consonants and alphabetizing. For extra practice, children should be encouraged to discover additional words that fit into each category.

Challenge:

This is a suggested activity or question related to the word that the activity focuses on. Some of these *Challenge* activities will require the simple knowledge of the scrambled word, while others will require a small amount of research. Any research should be able to be done on a computer, in an encyclopedia, or in a dictionary. The research should not take more than a few minutes and can be used as a way to learn more about the scrambled word or to enrich the child's knowledge.

If this is to be used as homework, allow the children to check their own activity sheets in class. Children can share words they have built, compare their words with those of their classmates, and share the answers to the *Challenge* questions. Encourage children to have fun exploring and building new words!

Possible Answers Found in the Activities: 1st Grade

1. stamp: am, as, at, map, mat, past/spat, pat/tap, sap, spat
2. swing: in, is, sign/sing, wig, win, wing
3. wagon: ago, an, go, gown, no/on, now/won/own, wag
4. apron: an, nap/pan, no/on, oar, or, ran
5. shovel: he, hoe, hole, hose/shoe, love, she, shoe, shove, so
6. earth: are, art/rat/tar, at, ate, ear, eat/tea, hat, he, hear, heart, heat, her, rat, rate, tea, tear, the
7. grade: age, are, dare/dear/read, drag, ear, gear, rag, read, red
8. paste: as, at, ate, east/seat, eat/tea, pat, pea, pest/step, pet, sap, sat, sea, set, tea
9. peace: ape/pea, cap, cape/pace, pea
10. arrow: oar, raw/war, roar, row, war
11. teach: act/cat, at, ate, cat, cheat, each, eat/tea, hat, he, heat, tea, the
12. bacon: an, cab, can, cob, no/on
13. beach: ace, ache/each, be, cab, each, he
14. bread: are, bad, bar, bare, be, bead, bear, beard, bed, dare/read/dear, drab, ear, read, red
15. candy: an, and, any, can, day
16. chase: ace, as, ash, case, cash, each, has, he, sea, she
17. clean: ace, an, can, lace, lane/lean
18. dance: ace, an, and, can, cane, den/end
19. drink: in, ink, kid, kind, rid, rink
20. house: hoe, hose, she, shoe, so, us, use
21. apple: ape/pea, lap/pal, leap/pale, pea
22. plant; an, ant/tan at, lap/pal, nap/pan, pant, pat/tap, plan, tan
23. party: art, at, part/trap, pat/tap, pay, pry, rat/tar, ray, tap, tar, trap, try, tray
24. brown: born, bow, no/on, now, own/won, rob, row, won, worn
25. smile (slime/limes): elm, is, lie, lime/mile, me, mile, slim
26. phone: he, hen, hoe, hop, hope, no/on, one, open, pen
27. toast: as, at, oat, sat, so, to
28. world: do, low, old, or, owl, rod, row, word
29. hotel: he, hole, hot, let, lot, the, to, toe
30. finger: fern, fig, fin, fine, fire, grin/ring, if, in, ring
31. mitten: in, it, item, me, men, met, mine, mint, net/ten, tent, time, tin
32. number: be, bum, bun, burn, me, men, menu, numb, rub, run
33. peanut: an, ant/tan, ape/pea, ate, aunt, eat/tea, nap/pan, neat, net/ten, nut, pan, pant, pat/tap, pea, pen, pet, put, tan, tape, tan, tap, tea, ten, tuna, tune, up
34. zipper: pie, pipe, prize, rip, ripe, zip, pier
35. donkey: den/end, do, doe, done, end, key, no/on, nod, on, one
36. crayon: acorn, an, any, arc/car, can, car, corn, cry, no/on, oar, on, or, ran, ray, yarn
37. people: eel, lop, lope/pole, peel, peep, plop
38. jacket: ace, act/cat, at, ate, cake, cat, eat/tea jack, jet, tack, take, tea
39. pillow: ill, lip, lop, low/owl, oil, owl, pill, plow
40. puppet: pet, pup, put, up
41. yellow: low/owl, owe, owl, we, well, yell
42. basket: as, ask, at, ate/eat/tea, bake, base, bat/tab, be, beak, beast, beat, best, bet, east/seat, sake, sat, sea, set, skate/steak, tab, take, task, tea
43. family: aim, am, fail, film, fly, if, lay, mail, may/yam, my, yam
44. friend: den/end, die, dine, fed, fern, fin, find, fine, fir, fire, fired/fried, if, in, red, ride
45. helped: deep, eel, he, heel, held, help, led, peel
46. ladder: add, are, dad, dare, dead, deal, dear/read, ear, lead, read, real, red
47. Monday: am, an, and, any, day, do, mad, man, many, may/yam, my, no, nod, on
48. ribbon: bib, bin, bob, born, in, iron, no/on, or, rib, rob, robin
49. summer: me, sue, sum, sure, us, use
50. teach: act/cat, at, ate/eat/tea, cat, cheat, each, hat, he, heat, the
51. across: as, car, cross, oar, or, scar, so, soar
52. animal: aim, am, an, in, mail, main, man, nail
53. danger (garden): age, an, and, are, dare, darn, dear/read, den, ear, earn, end, garden, gear, grade, grand, near, rag, range, read, red
54. return: net/ten, nut, rent, run, runt, ten, true, tune, turn
55. orange: age, ago, an, are/ear, earn, gear, go, gone, near, no/on, oar, on, or, rag, ran, rang
56. monkey: key, me, men, money, my, no/on, one
57. square: are, as, ear, sue/use, sure/user, us
58. person: no/on, nose, on, one, open, or, pen, pest, pose, rope
59. beaver: are, bare/bear, be, bear, bee, brave, ear, ever, verb
60. kitten: in, ink, it, kit, kite, net/ten, tent, tin
61. pocket: cot, kept, peck, pet, poet, poke, pot/top, to, toe, top

---

Name _____

Look For: | m | p | t | s | a |

Build It:

___ ___

___ ___

___ ___ ___

___ ___ ___

___ ___ ___

___ ___ ___ ___

___ ___ ___ ___

Focus On:

_a_ words

_____

_____

_____

_m_ words

_____

_____

_p_ words

_____

_____

What is the Scrambled Word?

___ ___ ___ ___ ___ ___

Challenge:

How much does it cost to mail a letter?

_____

Cut along dotted lines

Name _____

Look For:

i	g	n	w	s

Build It:

___ ___

___ ___

___ ___ ___

___ ___ ___

___ ___ ___ ___

___ ___ ___ ___

Focus On:

_i_ words

_____

_____

_s_ words

_____

_____

_w_ words

_____

_____

What is the Scrambled Word?

___ ___ ___ ___ ___ ___

Challenge:

What is your favorite thing to do on the playground?

_____

i g n w s

© Learning Resources, Inc.

Scrambled Word Building™ Activity Book

Cut along dotted lines

Name _____

Look For:

g	n	a	o	w

Build It:

___ ___

___ ___

___ ___

___ ___ ___

___ ___ ___

___ ___ ___

___ ___ ___ ___

Focus On:

_a_ words

_____

_____

_g_ words

_____

_____

_____

_n_ words

_____

_____

What is the Scrambled Word?

___ ___ ___ ___ ___

Challenge: Name three things you can pull.

_____

© Learning Resources, Inc.

Scrambled Word Building™ Activity Book

Cut along dotted lines

Name _____

Look For: | p | n | a | r | o |

Build It:

___ ___

___ ___

___ ___

___ ___ ___

___ ___ ___

___ ___ ___

Focus On:

_n_ words

_____

_____

_____

_o_ words

_____

_____

_____

_r_ words

_____

What is the Scrambled Word?

___ ___ ___ ___ ___ ___

Challenge:

What is your favorite meal to make?

_____

Cut along dotted lines

p

n

a

r

o

e

l l.

o

v

s

h e

Cut along dotted lines

Name _____

Look For:

h	s	v	o	l	e

Build It:

___ ___

___ ___

___ ___ ___

___ ___ ___ ___

___ ___ ___ ___

___ ___ ___ ___

___ ___ ___ ___ ___

Focus On: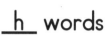

_h_ words

_____

_____

_____

_s_ words

_____

_____

_____

What is the Scrambled Word?

___ ___ ___ ___ ___ ___ ___

Challenge:

Name three ways you could dig a hole.

_____

© Learning Resources, Inc.   8   Scrambled Word Building™ Activity Book

Name _____

Look For: | r | h | t | a | e |

Build It:

_____ _____

_____ _____

_____ _____ _____

_____

_____

_____

_____ _____ _____

_____ _____ _____

_____ _____ _____ _____

_____ _____ _____ _____ _____

What is the Scrambled Word?

_____ _____ _____ _____ _____

Challenge:

How many planets are there in our solar system?

_____

Focus On:

__h_ words

_____

_____

_____

__t_ words

_____

_____

_____

__a_ words

_____

_____

_____

Cut along dotted lines

r

h

t

a

e

r

g

a

e

d

Cut along dotted lines

Name _____

Look For: | d | e | a | g | r |

Build It:

_____ _____ _____

_____ _____ _____

_____ _____ _____

_____ _____ _____ _____

_____ _____ _____ _____

_____ _____ _____ _____

What is the Scrambled Word?

_____ _____ _____ _____ _____

Challenge:

What is your best memory of 1st grade?

_____

Focus On:

_d_ words

_____

_____

_____

_r_ words

_____

_____

_____

Name _____

Look For: | t | e | s | p | a |

Build It:

___ ___

___ ___

___ ___ ___

___ ___ ___

___ ___ ___

___ ___ ___ ___

___ ___ ___ ___

___ ___ ___ ___

Focus On:

p_ **words**

_____

_____

_____

_____

s_ **words**

_____

_____

_____

_____

What is the Scrambled Word?

___ ___ ___ ___ ___

Challenge:

Name three things that are sticky.

_____

Cut along dotted lines

t

e

s

p

a

a

p.

e

e

c

Cut along dotted lines

Name _____

Look For: | c | e | e | p | a |

Build It: c a t

Focus On:

_p_ words

_____

_____

_c_ words

_____

_____

_____

_____

_____

_____

What is the Scrambled Word?

___ ___ ___ ___ ___

Challenge:

How would you help your friends get along if they were arguing over a toy?

_____

Name _____

Look For:

o	a	r	r	w

Build It: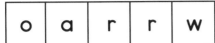

___ ___ ___

___ ___ ___

___ ___ ___

___ ___ ___ ___

Focus On:

_r_ words

_____

_____

_____

What is the Scrambled Word?

___ ___ ___ ___ ___

Challenge: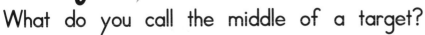

What do you call the middle of a target?

_____

© Learning Resources, Inc.   13   Scrambled Word Building™ Activity Book

Cut along dotted lines

O

a

r

r

w

Name _____

Look For: | e | a | t | h | c |

Build It:

_____ _____

_____ _____ _____

_____ _____ _____

_____ _____ _____

_____ _____ _____

_____ _____ _____ _____

_____ _____ _____ _____

Focus On:

__a__ words

_____

_____

_____

__h__ words

_____

_____

_____

What is the Scrambled Word?

_____ _____ _____ _____ _____

Challenge:

What is your favorite subject in school?

_____

Cut along dotted lines

Name _____

Look For: | n | o | c | a | b |

Build It:

____ ____

____ ____

____ ____ ____

____ ____ ____

____ ____ ____

Focus On:

_c_ words

_____

_____

_____

_n_ words

_____

_o_ words

_____

What is the Scrambled Word?

____ ____ ____ ____ ____

Challenge:

Name two things you might eat for breakfast.

_____

Cut along dotted lines

n

o

c

a

b

b.

a

e

h

c

Cut along dotted lines

Name _____

Look For: ⬡⬡ | c | h | e | a | b |

Build It: 🤲 c a t

_____ _____

_____ _____

_____ _____ _____

_____ _____ _____

_____ _____ _____ _____

What is the Scrambled Word?

_____ _____ _____ _____ _____

Focus On: 🔍

Alphabetical Order
Choose four words you have built and put them in alphabetical order below.

_____

_____

_____

_____

Challenge: 🏔️

Where is your favorite place to go in the summer?

_____

Name _____

Look For: | r | d | a | e | b |

Build It:

____ ____ ____

____ ____ ____

____ ____ ____

____ ____ ____

____ ____ ____ ____

____ ____ ____ ____

____

Focus On:

_b_ words

_____

_____

_____

_____

_d_ words

_____

_____

_____

_____

What is the Scrambled Word?

___ ___ ___ ___ ___

Challenge:

What ingredients are needed to make a peanut butter and jelly sandwich?

_____

r

d

a

e

Cut along dotted lines

b

a

c

d.

y

n.

Name _____

Look For: | n | y | d | c | a |

Build It:

Focus On:

_a_ words

_____

_____

_____

___ ___ ___

___ ___ ___

___ ___ ___

___ ___ ___

What is the Scrambled Word?

___ ___ ___ ___ ___

Challenge:

If you could invent a new lollipop flavor, what would
it be?

_____

Cut along dotted lines

Name _____

Look For: | s | h | c | a | e |

Build It:

____ ____

____ ____

____ ____ ____

____ ____ ____

____ ____ ____

____ ____ ____ ____

____ ____ ____ ____

____ ____ ____

Focus On:

_a_ words

_____

_____

_____

_c_ words

_____

_____

_s_ words

_____

_____

What is the Scrambled Word?

____ ____ ____ ____ ____

Challenge:

What is your favorite outside game to play?

_____

s

h

c

a

e

Cut along dotted lines

Name _____

Look For: | n | l | e | c | a |

Build It:

Focus On:

_a_ words

_____

_____

_l_ words

_____

_____

_____

___ ___ ___

___ ___ ___ ___

___ ___ ___ ___

___ ___ ___ ___

What is the Scrambled Word?

___ ___ ___ ___ ___

Challenge:

What are your chores at home?

_____

© Learning Resources, Inc.

Scrambled Word Building™ Activity Book

Cut along dotted lines

Name _____

Look For: | e | d | c | a | n |

Build It:

___ ___

___ ___ ___

___ ___ ___

___ ___ ___

___ ___ ___ ___

Focus On:

__a__ words

_____

_____

_____

__c__ words

_____

_____

What is the Scrambled Word?

___ ___ ___ ___ ___

Challenge:

Have you ever been in a recital or show?
Tell about it.

_____

_____

_____

Cut along dotted lines

e

d

c

a

n

r

Name _____

Look For: k | n | d | i | r

Build It:

i

d

n

k

_____ _____

_____ _____ _____

_____ _____ _____

_____ _____ _____

_____ _____ _____ _____

What is the Scrambled Word?

_____ _____ _____ _____ _____ _____

Challenge:

Food is to hungry as _____ is to thirsty.

_____

Focus On:

_i_ words

_____

_____

_k_ words

_____

_____

_r_ words

_____

_____

Cut along dotted lines

Name _____

Look For: | s | o | h | u | e |

Build It:

___ ___

___ ___

___ ___ ___

___ ___ ___

___ ___ ___ ___

___ ___ ___ ___

Focus On:

__s__ words

_____

_____

_____

__h__ words

_____

_____

What is the Scrambled Word?

___ ___ ___ ___ ___ ___

Challenge:

Name three places people could live.

_____

Cut along dotted lines

s

o

h

u

e

e

a

l . i

p . i

p

Name _____

Look For: | p | p | l | a | e |

Build It:

— — —

— — —

— — —

— — — —

— — — —

Focus On:

p words
_____
_____
_____

l words
_____
_____

What is the Scrambled Word?

— — — — — —

Cut along dotted lines

Challenge:

Name three fruits that grow on trees.

_____

Name _____

Look For: [t] [n] [l] [p] [a]

Build It:

_____ _____

_____ _____

_____ _____ _____

_____ _____ _____

_____ _____ _____

_____ _____ _____ _____

_____ _____ _____ _____

Focus On:

p words

_____

_____

_____

_____

a words

_____

_____

_____

What is the Scrambled Word?

_____ _____ _____ _____ _____ _____

Challenge:
What does a flower need to grow?

_____

t

n

l

p

a

Cut along dotted lines

Name _____

Look For: 👓

y	p	t	r	a

Build It: 🖐 c a t 🖐

___ ___

___ ___ ___

___ ___ ___

___ ___ ___

___ ___ ___

___ ___ ___ ___

___ ___ ___ ___

___ ___ ___ ___

Focus On: 🔍

_p_ words

_____

_____

_____

_____

_t_ words

_____

_____

_____

_____

What is the Scrambled Word?

___ ___ ___ ___ ___ ___

Challenge: 🏔

What was your favorite birthday? Tell about it.

_____

_____

(left margin, vertical) a r t p y

(left margin, vertical) Cut along dotted lines

Name _____

Activity 24

Look For: | w | b | o | n | r |

Build It:

____ ____

____ ____

____ ____ ____

____ ____ ____

____ ____ ____

____ ____ ____ ____

____ ____ ____ ____

Focus On:

_b_ words

_____

_____

_n_ words

_____

_____

_r_ words

_____

_____

What is the Scrambled Word?

__ __ __ __ __

Challenge:

What are three colors a bear might be?

_____

w

b

o

n

r

Cut along dotted lines

© Learning Resources, Inc.   27   Scrambled Word Building™ Activity Book

Name _____

Look For: 👓

l	s	m	e	i

Build It: 🖐️ c a t

___ ___

___ ___

___ ___ ___

___ ___ ___

___ ___ ___ ___

___ ___ ___ ___

___ ___ ___ ___

Focus On: 🔍

_l_ words

_____

_____

_m_ words

_____

_____

_s_ words

_____

_____

What is the Scrambled Word?

___ ___ ___ ___ ___

Challenge: 🏔️

Write five things that make you happy.

_____

_____

© Learning Resources, Inc.

Scrambled Word Building™ Activity Book

Cut along dotted lines

i

e

m

s

l

Name _____

Look For: | n | o | h | p | e |

Build It:

___ ___

___ ___

___ ___

___ ___ ___

___ ___ ___

___ ___ ___

___ ___ ___

___ ___ ___

Focus On:

_h_ words

_____

_____

_____

_____

_o_ words

_____

_____

_____

What is the Scrambled Word?

___ ___ ___ ___ ___

Challenge:

What is your telephone number?

_____

© Learning Resources, Inc. 29 Scrambled Word Building™ Activity Book

n   o   h   p   e

Name _____

Look For: 👓

s	t	a	o	t

Build It: 🖐️c a t

Focus On: 🔍

_a_ words

_____

_____

_s_ words

_____

_____

_____ _____

_____ _____

_____ _____

_____ _____

_____ _____ _____

_____ _____ _____

What is the Scrambled Word?

_____ _____ _____ _____ _____

Challenge: 🏔️

Name three things you can find in the kitchen.

_____

Cut along dotted lines

t o a t s

Name _____

Look For: d o r w l

Build It:

____ ____

____ ____

____ ____ ____

____ ____ ____

____ ____ ____

____ ____ ____ ____ ____

What is the Scrambled Word?

____ ____ ____ ____ ____

Focus On:

_o_ words

_____

_____

_____

_r_ words

_____

_____

Challenge:

What is the name of the planet we live on?

_____

Cut along dotted lines

d

o

r

w

l

Name _____

Look For: | e | l | o | h | t |

Build It:

_____ _____

_____ _____

_____ _____ _____

_____ _____ _____ _____

_____ _____ _____ _____

_____ _____ _____

_____ _____ _____ _____

Focus On:

_h_ words

_____

_____

_____

_t_ words

_____

_____

_____

What is the Scrambled Word?

_____ _____ _____ _____ _____

Challenge:

Have you ever been away on a vacation? Where did you go?

_____

© Learning Resources, Inc.

Scrambled Word Building™ Activity Book

Cut along dotted lines

Name _____

Look For: | g | i | r | e | f | n |

Build It:

Focus On:

_f_ words

_____

_____

_____

_____

_____

_____

_____

_____

_____

_____

What is the Scrambled Word?

_ _ _ _ _ _ _

Challenge:

How many fingers and toes would triplets have all together?

_____

g

i

r

e

f

n

Cut along dotted lines

m e t n i t

Name _____

Look For:

t	i	n	t	e	m

Build It:

____ ____

____ ____

____ ____ ____

____ ____ ____

____ ____ ____

____ ____ ____

____ ____ ____ ____

____ ____ ____ ____

____ ____ ____ ____

Focus On:

_m_ words

_____

_____

_____

_____

_t_ words

_____

_____

_____

_____

What is the Scrambled Word?

____ ____ ____ ____ ____ ____

Cut along dotted lines

Challenge:

What is the difference between gloves and mittens?

_____

© Learning Resources, Inc.

Scrambled Word Building™ Activity Book

Name _____

Look For: | b | r | u | m | n | e |

Build It:

___ ___

___ ___ ___

___ ___ ___

___ ___ ___

___ ___ ___

___ ___ ___ ___

___ ___ ___ ___

Focus On:

_b_ words

_____

_____

_____

_m_ words

_____

_____

_____

What is the Scrambled Word?

___ ___ ___ ___ ___ ___ ___

Challenge:

How many days are there in a week?

_____

Cut along dotted lines

b

r

u

m

n

e

e

u.

p.

n.

a

t

Cut along dotted lines

Name _____

Look For:

t	a	n	p	u	e

Build It:

____ ____

____ ____

____ ____ ____

____ ____ ____

____ ____ ____

____ ____ ____

____ ____ ____ ____

____ ____ ____

____ ____ ____

____ ____ ____ ____

Focus On:

_a_ words

_____

_____

_____

_____

_p_ words

_____

_____

_____

_____

What is the Scrambled Word?

____ ____ ____ ____ ____ ____ ____

 Challenge:

Name three kinds of nuts.

_____

© Learning Resources, Inc.   Scrambled Word Building™ Activity Book

Name _____

Look For: | r | z | p | i | e | p |

Build It:

Focus On:

_p_ words

_____

_____

_____

_r_ words

_____

_____

___ ___ ___

___ ___ ___

___ ___ ___ ___

___ ___ ___ ___ ___

What is the Scrambled Word?

___ ___ ___ ___ ___ ___

Challenge:

Tie is to shoe as zip is to _____.

Cut along dotted lines

r

z

p

i

e

p

d.

y

n.

e

o

k.

Cut along dotted lines

Name _____

Look For: | k | o | e | n | y | d |

Build It:

_____ _____

_____ _____

_____ _____ _____

_____ _____ _____

_____ _____ _____

_____ _____ _____

_____ _____ _____

Focus On:

_d_ words

_____

_____

_____

_____

_n_ words

_____

_____

What is the Scrambled Word?

_____ _____ _____ _____ _____ _____

 **Challenge:**

What animal, other than a dog or cat, would you like to have for a pet?

_____

Name _____

Look For: | y | r | o | n | a | c |

Build It:

____ ____

____ ____

____ ____ ____

____ ____ ____

____ ____ ____

____ ____ ____ ____

____ ____ ____

____ ____ ____ ____ ____

Focus On:

_a_ words

_____

_____

_____

_____

_c_ words

_____

_____

_____

_____

What is the Scrambled Word?

____ ____ ____ ____ ____ ____

Challenge:

What is your favorite color? Name three things that are that color.

_____

© Learning Resources, Inc.

Scrambled Word Building™ Activity Book

y

r

o

n.

a

c

Cut along dotted lines

o

l

p

p

e

e

Name _____

Look For:

e	e	p	p	l	o

Build It:

Focus On:

_p_ words

_____ _____ _____

_____ _____ _____

_____ _____ _____ _____

_____ _____ _____

_____ _____ _____

_____

_____

_____

_____

What is the Scrambled Word?

_____ _____ _____ _____ _____ _____

Cut along dotted lines

Challenge:

Name two differences between humans and dogs.

_____

Name _____

Look For:

e	k	c	t	a	j

Build It:

Focus On:

 _a_ words

_____

_____

_____

_____

 _t_ words

_____

_____

_____

__ __ __

__ __ __

__ __ __

__ __ __

__ __ __ __

__ __ __ __

What is the Scrambled Word?

__ __ __ __ __ __ __

Challenge: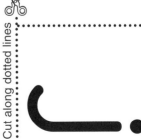

Name three things you would wear in cold weather.

_____

Cut along dotted lines

e

k

c

t

a

j

Name _____

Look For:

w	p	l	l	i	o

Build It:

___ ___ ___

___ ___ ___

___ ___ ___

___ ___ ___

___ ___ ___ ___

Focus On:

l words

_____

_____

_____

p words

_____

_____

What is the Scrambled Word?

___ ___ ___ ___ ___ ___ ___

Challenge:

Give exact directions on how to make a bed.

_____

_____

Cut along dotted lines

Name _____

Look For:

p	p	p	t	e	u

Build It:

_____ _____

_____ _____ _____

_____ _____ _____

_____ _____ _____

Focus On:

p̶ words

_____

_____

_____

_____

What is the Scrambled Word?

___ ___ ___ ___ ___ ___

Challenge:
Was Pinocchio a real boy?

_____

p

p

p

t

e

u

Cut along dotted lines

Name _____

Look For:

w	l	l	y	e	o

Build It:

__ __

__ __ __

__ __ __

__ __ __

__ __ __ __

Focus On:

o words

_____

_____

w words

_____

_____

What is the Scrambled Word?

__ __ __ __ __ __

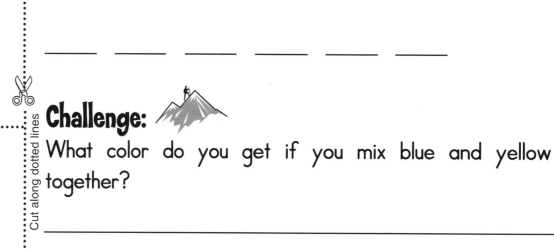

Challenge:

What color do you get if you mix blue and yellow together?

_____

© Learning Resources, Inc.

Scrambled Word Building™ Activity Book

Cut along dotted lines

o

e

y

l

l

w

Name _____

Look For:  | k | s | a | b | t | e |

Build It:

_____ _____

_____ _____

_____

_____ _____ _____

_____

_____

_____

_____ _____ _____

_____ _____

_____ _____ _____

_____ _____ _____ _____ _____

Focus On:

_a_ words

_____

_____

_____

_____

_b_ words

_____

_____

_____

_____

What is the Scrambled Word?

___ ___ ___ ___ ___ ___ ___

Challenge:

What foods would you like to have on a picnic?

_____

© Learning Resources, Inc.
Scrambled Word Building™ Activity Book

k

s

a

b

t

e

Cut along dotted lines ✂

a

m

f

i

y

i

Name _____

Look For:

l	y	i	f	m	a

Build It: 🖐️ c a t

___ ___

___

___ ___ ___

___ ___ ___

___ ___ ___

___ ___ ___ ___

Focus On: 🔍

_f_ words

_____

_____

_____

_____

_m_ words

_____

_____

_____

What is the Scrambled Word?

___ ___ ___ ___ ___ ___ ___

Challenge:

How many cousins do you have?

_____

© Learning Resources, Inc.   Scrambled Word Building™ Activity Book

Cut along dotted lines

Name _____

Look For: | i | f | r | d | n | e |

Build It:

_____ _____

_____

_____ _____ _____

_____

_____

_____ _____ _____ _____

_____ _____ _____ _____

_____ _____ _____

_____ _____ _____ _____ _____

Focus On:

_d_ words

_____

_____

_____

_f_ words

_____

_____

_____

_r_ words

_____

_____

What is the Scrambled Word?

___ ___ ___ ___ ___ ___

Challenge:

How could you make a new student feel welcome?

i

f

r

d

n

e

Cut along dotted lines

h

d.

e

e

l.

p.

Name _____

Look For: | p | l | e | e | d | h |

Build It:

Focus On: 🔍

_h_ words

_____

_____

_____

_____

— — —

— — — —

— — — —

— — — — —

— — — — —

What is the Scrambled Word?

— — — — — — —

✂ Cut along dotted lines

Challenge:

Name three ways you can help your teacher.

_____

© Learning Resources, Inc.   Scrambled Word Building™ Activity Book

Name _____

Look For: | r | a | d | d | e | l |

Build It:

Focus On:

_d_ words

_____
_____
_____

_r_ words

_____
_____
_____

_____ _____ _____

_____ _____ _____

_____ _____ _____

_____ _____ _____ _____

_____ _____ _____ _____

_____ _____ _____ _____

What is the Scrambled Word?

_____ _____ _____ _____ _____ _____

Challenge:

Name three things you climb.

_____

r
a
d
d
e
l

m

a

d

y

o

n

Name _____

Look For:

n	o	y	d	a	m

Build It:

___ ___

___ ___

___ ___

___ ___ ___

___ ___ ___

___ ___ ___

___ ___ ___ ___

Focus On:

_a_ words

_____

_____

_____

_____

_m_ words

_____

_____

_____

_____

What is the Scrambled Word?

___ ___ ___ ___ ___ ___

✂ Cut along dotted lines

Challenge:

What is your favorite day of the week? Why?

_____

© Learning Resources, Inc.   Scrambled Word Building™ Activity Book

Name _____

Look For: | b | b | n | i | o | r |

Build It:

___ ___

___ ___

___ ___ ___

___ ___ ___

___ ___ ___

___ ___ ___ ___

___ ___ ___ ___

___ ___ ___ ___ ___ ___

Focus On:

_b_ words

_____

_____

_____

_____

_r_ words

_____

_____

_____

What is the Scrambled Word?

___ ___ ___ ___ ___ ___ ___

Challenge:

Name three things that you use to wrap a present.

_____

Cut along dotted lines

b

b

n

i

o

r

Name _____

Look For:

u	r	m	m	e	s

Build It:

___ ___

___ ___

___ ___ ___

___ ___ ___

___ ___ ___ ___

Focus On:

_s_ words

_____

_____

_____

_u_ words

_____

_____

What is the Scrambled Word?

___ ___ ___ ___ ___ ___

Challenge:

What is your favorite season? Why?

_____

_____

© Learning Resources, Inc.

Scrambled Word Building™ Activity Book

Cut along dotted lines

s

e

m

m

r

u.

Name _____

Look For: 👓 | t | h | c | e | a |

Build It: 🤲

___ ___

___ ___

___ ___ ___

___ ___ ___

___ ___ ___

___ ___ ___

___ ___ ___ ___

___ ___ ___ ___

___ ___ ___ ___ ___

Focus On: 🔍

Alphabetical Order
Choose five words you have built and put them in alphabetical order below.

_____

_____

_____

_____

_____

What is the Scrambled Word?

___ ___ ___ ___ ___

Challenge: ⛰️

What do you want to be when you grow up? Why?

_____

t

h

c

e

a

Cut along dotted lines

r

o

s

c

a

s

Cut along dotted lines

Name _____

Look For:

s	a	c	s	o	r

Build It:

____ ____

Focus On:

_c_ words

_____

_____

_s_ words

_____

_____

_____

____ ____

____ ____

____ ____ ____

____ ____ ____ ____

____ ____ ____ ____ ____

What is the Scrambled Word?

____ ____ ____ ____ ____ ____ ____

Challenge:

What should you do before you cross a street?

_____

© Learning Resources, Inc.

Scrambled Word Building™ Activity Book

Name _____

Look For: | n | a | i | l | a | m |

Build It:

___ ___

___ ___

___ ___

___ ___ ___

___ ___ ___ ___

___ ___ ___ ___

Focus On:

__a_ words

_____

_____

_____

__m_ words

_____

_____

_____

What is the Scrambled Word?

___ ___ ___ ___ ___ ___

Challenge:

Carrot is to vegetable as dog is to_____.

© Learning Resources, Inc.

Scrambled Word Building™ Activity Book

n

a

i

l

a

m

Name _____

Look For:

r	a	d	e	g	n

Build It:

____ ____

____ ____ ____

____ ____ ____

____ ____ ____

____ ____ ____ ____

____ ____ ____

____ ____ ____

____ ____ ____ ____

____ ____ ____ ____ ____

Focus On:

_a_ words

_____

_____

_____

_____

_g_ words

_____

_____

_____

_____

What is the Scrambled Word?

____ ____ ____ ____ ____ ____

Challenge:
Name three safety tips.

_____

n. g e d. a r

Name _____

Look For: | t | e | r | n | r | u |

Build It:

___ ___ ___

___ ___ ___

___ ___ ___

___ ___ ___ ___

___ ___ ___ ___

___ ___ ___ ___

Focus On:

_t_ words

_____

_____

_____

_____

_r_ words

_____

_____

_____

What is the Scrambled Word?

___ ___ ___ ___ ___ ___

Challenge:

Have you ever had to take something back to a store? Why did you have to bing it back?

_____

_____

Cut along dotted lines

t

e

r

n

r

u

r

n

g

o

e

a

Cut along dotted lines

Name _____

Look For: | a | e | o | g | n | r |

Build It:

___ ___

___ ___

___ ___

___ ___ ___

___ ___ ___

___ ___ ___

___ ___ ___ ___

___ ___ ___ ___

___ ___ ___

Focus On:

_a_ words

_____

_____

_____

_____

_g_ words

_____

_____

_____

What is the Scrambled Word?

___ ___ ___ ___ ___ ___

 Challenge:

What color do you get when you mix red and yellow together?

_____

© Learning Resources, Inc.   Scrambled Word Building™ Activity Book

Name _____

Look For: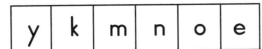

y	k	m	n	o	e

Build It:

____ ____

____ ____

____ ____

____ ____ ____

____ ____ ____

Focus On: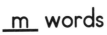

_m_ words

_____

_____

_____

_____

_o_ words

_____

_____

____ ____ ____ ____

What is the Scrambled Word?

____ ____ ____ ____ ____ ____

Challenge: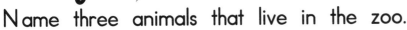

Name three animals that live in the zoo.

_____

© Learning Resources, Inc.   59   Scrambled Word Building™ Activity Book

y k m n o e

r

a

s

u.

e

q.

Name _____

Look For:

q	e	u	s	a	r

Build It:

____ ____

____ ____

____ ____ ____

____ ____ ____

____ ____ ____

____ ____ ____

Focus On:

Alphabetical Order
Choose four words you have built and put them in alphabetical order below.

_____

_____

_____

_____

What is the Scrambled Word?

____ ____ ____ ____ ____ ____

Challenge:

Name three things that are shaped like a box.

_____

© Learning Resources, Inc.

Scrambled Word Building™ Activity Book

Name _____

Look For: | o | p | r | e | n | s |

Build It:

_____ _____

_____ _____

_____ _____ _____

_____ _____

_____ _____ _____

_____ _____ _____

_____ _____ _____

Focus On:

_o_ words

_____

_____

_____

_____

_p_ words

_____

_____

_____

What is the Scrambled Word?

___ ___ ___ ___ ___ ___ ___

Challenge:

Who is someone you admire? Why?

_____

_____

o

p

r

e

n

s

Cut along dotted lines

Name _____

Look For:

v	r	e	b	a	e

Build It:

___ ___

_____ _____

_____ _____ _____

_____ _____ _____

_____ _____ _____

_____ _____ _____ _____

_____ _____ _____ _____ _____

Focus On:

_b_ words

_____

_____

_____

_____

_e_ words

_____

_____

What is the Scrambled Word?

___ ___ ___ ___ ___ ___

Challenge:

Name three animals that live in or near a river.

_____

Cut along dotted lines

e

a

b.

e

r

v

Name _____

Look For: | n | e | t | k | i | t |

Build It:

_____ _____

_____ _____ _____

_____ _____ _____

_____ _____ _____

_____ _____ _____ _____

_____ _____ _____ _____

Focus On:

_k_ words

_____

_____

_t_ words

_____

_____

_i_ words

_____

_____

_____

What is the Scrambled Word?

_____ _____ _____ _____ _____ _____

Challenge:

What famous nursery rhyme characters lost their mittens?

_____

Cut along dotted lines

c

e

k

p

t

o

Cut along dotted lines

Name _____

Look For:

o	t	p	k	e	c

Build It:

___ ___

___ ___ ___

___ ___ ___

___ ___ ___

___ ___ ___ ___

___ ___ ___ ___

Focus On:

_p_ words

_____

_____

_____

_____

_t_ words

_____

_____

_____

_____

What is the Scrambled Word?

___ ___ ___ ___ ___ ___ ___

Challenge:

Name three places people might keep their money.

_____

_____